PRAISE FOR CAREER INFOPRENEUR'S SUCCESS ROADMAP

"Only a small percentage of coaches make their living at it, but what most don't understand, is that those who *do* make a good living at coaching, do so by having multiple revenue streams. Marcia's formula for coaching 2.0 *is* how the coaches who have 'made it' do it. And Marcia has made it *big*. Listen to her advice and follow it. Whether your goal is to make a million dollars or to just meet your old job's income, this book will lead you to the bank. And then some! " -- Laura Berman Fortgang, MCC, founder of Now What? Coaching and author of *Now What? 90 Days to a New Life Direction*, *Living Your Best Life* and *Take Yourself to the Top*

"My first comment about Marcia Bench's new book "Career Infopreneur's Success Roadmap," is 'Where was this book 10 years agao when I started my business?' I would have saved thousands of dollars and so much stress if I had been able to have this book as my guide to infopreneurship.

This book says it all. I began reading the book with the intent of reading a few pages and found that I couldn't stop reading. Marcia presents her ideas in an easy-to-read style that entices you to want more information without wading through a great deal of theory.

I highly recommend this book to anyone who is starting out or who is thinking of moving to that next plateau of coaching. It's all here in one book. Congratulations to Marcia for writing such a comprehensive book for coaches." -- Carole Martin, The Interview Coach, http://wwwinterviewcoach.com

"Bench is a visionary and leader in the field of career coaching and now gives us a great gift of understanding where career coaching is headed and how to shift to info being an infopreneur. This book will transform your career coaching business and keep you ahead of the curve!" -- Terri Levine, PhD, MCC, author of *The Successful Coach*
http://www.CoachInstitute.Com

"Capitalizing on her many years of success as a career coach and infopreneur, Marcia Bench has developed a roadmap that career coaches can easily follow for their own businesses. Marcia's original concept of Career Coaching 2.0 is fascinating, as she guides readers through the nine steps for creating a successful business as an infopreneur. I'm delighted that Marcia included two elements that are essential for an effective roadmap: information that is both practical *and* pragmatic. This is her best book yet!" -- Syl Leduc, MEd, MPEC, Certified Executive Coach, Founder and Former President of Client Compass Software for Coaches, http://www.SageLeaders.com

"I wish I'd had all this great information when I was starting out! Life would have been a lot less stressful, and I would have had a much clearer idea what I needed to do, how to do it, and where to find the right help." -- Carrie Gallant, President, Gallant Solutions, Inc., Vancouver, BC

"Marcia Bench has quickly become the *go to expert* on career coaching....and this book is an evolutionary step in how to carve out a lucrative career coaching business. Marcia gives you the perspective, the research, and the tools and map to complete your journey into career coaching. This book will guide you into being an infopreneur in an ever-changing world with people who change careers several times in their lifetime. What a huge market. Combine the specifics of career coaching with the whole person approach of total life coaching and you can serve your clients well and enjoy what you do for your own career." -- Dr. Patrick Williams, MCCC, Chief Energizing Officer, Institute for Life Coach Training http://www.lifecoachtraining.com

 "The truth is that career coaching is different than other types of coaching. If you want to make a lucrative career out of career coaching, then stop right here because no one on the planet understand the needs of clients, the marketplace conditions, and what it takes to succeed as a career coach better than Marcia Bench! This book is a must read for career coaches." --Christian Mickelsen, CEO of the Coaching Business Rocket Launcher http://www.CoachingBusinessRocketLauncher.com

"Marcia Bench has distilled the essence of successful career infopreneurship into a system that works. Here is valuable info for anyone who wants to make it online with a successful, thriving coaching business. Right on, Marcia!" -- Suzanne Falter-Barns, www.getknownnow.com

"Learn how to earn 7 figures while enjoying your life and work--in 9 simple steps. Don't miss this practical guide to become a career infopreneur. Take the advice of Marcia Bench, someone who has done it and knows the quick path to all-around success." -- Susan Harrow, Media Coach, CEO of PRsecrets.com and author of *Sell Yourself Without Selling Your Soul*

"If you are even thinking about creating a career information product, you'll do well to invest in Marcia Bench's Career Infopreneur's Success Roadmap. Her thorough, content-rich road map will save you time, money, and frustration each step of the way." -- Carol McClelland, PhD, Transition Dynamics Enterprises, Inc. www.transitiondynamics.com

"Marcia Bench's fascinating real-life story about how she built her career coaching business is reason enough to buy this book! Her story will inspire you if you want to break out on your own or take your current business to the next level. There is plenty of solid advice for anyone interested in career coaching or using information to grow a highly-successful business!" -- Stephanie Chandler, Small business expert and author of *From Entrepreneur to Infopreneur: Make*

Money with Books, eBooks and Information Products
www.BusinessInfoGuide.com

"Too many career professionals struggle to build businesses one client at a time. With Marcia's road map to infopreneurship, you can break out of this trap and build a thriving, sustainable business that will allow you to impact the lives of more people than you ever could working one-on-one." -- C.J. Hayden, MCC, CPCC, Author, *Get Clients Now!* and *Get Hired Now!*

CAREER INFOPRENEUR'S SUCCESS ROADMAP

WORKBOOK

9 Proven Steps to More Income, More Freedom and More Clients

Marcia Bench

Career Infopreneur's Success Roadmap – The Workbook
Published by High Flight Press 2008

This publication is designed to provide accurate and authoritative information in regard to the subject matter covered. It is sold with the understanding that the publisher is not engaged in rendering professional services. If legal, accounting, medical, psychological, or any other expert assistance is required, the services of a competent professional person should be sought. Author and publisher specifically disclaim any liability for the reader's use of any forms or advice provided in this book. It is not warranted as fit for any specific use or purpose, but is intended to give general information that is as current as possible as of the date of publication.

Library of Congress Cataloging-in-Publication Data:

Bench, Marcia
      Career Infopreneur's Success Roadmap
      / Marcia Bench
      ISBN   978-0-9817005-2-6   (10 digit: 0-9817005-2-7)
      1.   Entrepreneurship 2. Home Based Business 3. Marketing 4. Career counseling

Printed in the United States of America

Career Infopreneur's Success Roadmap: 9 Proven Steps to More Income, More Freedom and More Clients

TABLE OF CONTENTS

PART ONE:

PREPARING

CHAPTER 1
Career Coaching 2.0: What is a Career Infopreneur?

Your Story

You have read Marcia's story of arriving at the "career infopreneur" model (pp. 2-3 *Career Infopreneur's Success Roadmap*). What is *your* story that has brought you to start your career infopreneur business now, or to change your approach *to* an infopreneur model? Write it here.

_____

_____

_____

_____

_____

_____

_____

_____

_____

_____

_____

_____

_____

_____

In just the past few years, the career coaching business model has evolved from "Career Coaching 1.0" to "Career Coaching 2.0" (p. 3-5 text). The following table illustrates the differences between the two:

Career Coaching 1.0 vs. 2.0

Aspect	Career Coaching 1.0: Coaching	Career Coaching 2.0: Infopreneur
Focus	1:1 coaching	Solution to shared client problem
Marketing objective	Marketing to sell coaching	Two-step marketing to sell product first, then coaching package
Difficulty	Hard work	Much easier!
Mode of service delivery	Personal service delivery	Virtual/leveraged service delivery
Revenue/growth opportunities	Limited $/ growth opportunities	Unlimited $/ growth opportunities
Difficulty establishing expert status	Difficult to establish your expert status	Easy to establish your expert status

Which model most characterizes your business? Use the self-assessment that follows to decide.

Career Coaching 2.0 Quiz

Statement	1 (not true)	2 (some-what true)	3 (always true)
1. My business focuses primarily on communicating a solution to a shared client problem, in a variety of services and media.			
2. My marketing asks prospects to first opt in to obtain an info product or other "sample" of my services, with coaching as an add-on or upsell.			
3. I find building my business relatively easy, with much of it coming by referral or customer request.			
4. I use the internet extensively in delivering my services.			
5. I have leveraged my expertise through mentoring or licensing others, productizing some of my content, developing a coaching team, or otherwise, so that I only deliver as much of the services as I choose to.			
6. My business is not limited by the "time for dollars" model – I provide at least as much of my services via passive means as by active "real time" means.			
7. I am perceived as an expert, celebrity, or "guru" by my target market/clientele.			
8. I have created at least one info product that I am actively selling.			
9. I have at least one month-to month continuity/membership program to which interested prospects and customers can subscribe.			
10. I frequently deliver both sales calls and paid coaching and information calls to groups, versus 1:1.			
TOTAL:			

Scoring:

24-30: Congratulations - you have incorporated a Career Coaching 2.0/Infopreneur approach!

15-23: Your business has a few aspects of Career Coaching 2.0 but need further development

10-14: Keep reading – you need to move out of Career Coaching 2.0 as soon as possible!

What is a Career Infopreneur?

Fill in the missing components of the definition of career infopreneur below:

"A career infopreneur is an _____ entrepreneur who specializes in a _____ related to career, _____, job or employment." (p. 7 text)

The primary function or role of a career infopreneur is to _____ a problem shared by a _____ group of people." (p. 8 text)

The primary reason 90 percent of coaches have not achieved revenues of at least $100,000 in their business is because they are offering coaching as a _____-_____ service.   (p. 9 text)

Why Career Infopreneurship?

The three primary reasons career infopreneurship is in such demand are (pp. 11-14 text):

1. _____

2. _____

3. _____

Traits for Success as a Top Career Infopreneur

Do you have what it takes to be successful as a career infopreneur? Take the quiz below to find out.

QUIZ: IS CAREER INFOPRENEURSHIP FOR YOU?

Question	Yes	No
1. Is it important to you to accomplish something meaningful with your life?	✓	
2. Do you want to help others and make a contribution through your work?	✓	
3. Would you like to be famous in your area of expertise?	✓	
4. Do you typically set both short- and long-term goals for yourself?	✓	
5. Are you persistent enough to usually achieve your goals?	✓	
6. Do you enjoy working on your own?		✓
7. Do you like to perform a variety of tasks in your job?	✓	
8. Are you self-disciplined?	✓	
9. Do you like to be in control of your working environment?	✓	
10. Do you take full responsibility for your successes *and* failures?	✓	
11. Can you place the needs of your business above your family when necessary?		✓
12. Are you in excellent physical, mental and emotional health?	✓	
13. Do you have the drive and energy to create a successful business?	✓	
14. Do you have a basic knowledge of the workplace of today?	✓	
15. Have you ever been so engrossed in your work that time passed unnoticed?	✓	
16. Do you consider "failures" as opportunities to learn and grow?	✓	
17. Can you hold to your ideas and goals even when others disagree with you?	✓	
18. Are you willing to take moderate risks to achieve your goals?	✓	
19. Can you afford to lose the money you invest in your business?	✓	
20. When the need arises, are you willing to do a job that may not interest you?	✓	
21. Are you willing to work hard to acquire new skills?	✓	
22. Do you enjoy helping people brainstorm new options for which there may not be an existing model?	✓	

Evaluating Your Answers:

18-22 "yes"   Career infopreneurship is for you!

14-18 "yes"   You may be suited to career infopreneurship

10-14 "yes"   Work within a team or organization may be a better fit than self-employment

5-10 "yes"   Carefully examine your choice to be sure career infopreneurship is what you want to do!

0-5 "yes"   Career infopreneurship is probably *not* your best career choice

CHAPTER 2
Step 1: Defining Your Intended Audience and Relating to Today's Workers

Now that you realize Market must precede Message, please complete the following exercises to clearly define your target market.

1. Industries in which I have worked (examples: software production, medical products sales, data processing, government, retail computer sales):

Directory Publishing, Toner Sales,
Car Marketing, Cleaning,
Pet Sitting, Clothing Retail

2. Positions I have held in past jobs (example: sales manager, production technician, plumber, consultant, vice president of international trade):

Sales Executive
Marketing Executive
Marketing Administrator
Sales Secretary
Marketing Secretary

3. Communities, clubs, societies, religious organizations, or other groups in which I have connections:

Wellington Sports Club
California Football Club
Wokingham Gossip Girls
Facebook

4. Age group or a gender (male versus female) or any other special trait that I particularly resonate with:

_____ females who have had children _____

_____

_____

_____

_____

_____

5. My geographical area of preference, if any:

_____

_____

_____

_____

_____

_____

4.   Religious, political, philosophical or other psychographic characteristics shared by the people I most enjoy serving, doing business with, or being around:

Positive People

Enthusiastic

Intelligent

Articulate

Motivated

Friendly.

Fair.

5. Traits my customers or clients would have if I could hand-pick them (and you can!):

Same as 4.

_____

_____

_____

_____

_____

_____

NOTE: Niches derived from the above questions are *natural* niches or target markets. You can also target an as yet unfamiliar niche by ensuring that they are identifiable, economically reachable, and have big issues or problems that your expertise could help them solve.

There are two ways to view a niche:
   a) **Horizontal:** an expertise niche (e.g., bookkeeping services for small businesses, career coaching services, etc.) – harder to achieve significant penetration, takes longer to do
   b) **Vertical:** a group of people with a similar problem or set of problems (e.g., independent exercise equipment retailers, fee-based financial planners) – this type of niche is much easier to penetrate

Tip: apply your horizontal expertise to a vertical niche to jump-start your business fast! Example: David Frey – pool and spa retailers – achieved 80% penetration in just 12 months

Narrative description of my target as I now understand/view them:

Female marketing or Sales Professionals wanting to start their own businesses Around A family.

Testing My Target Market

A. Specificity:

Is my market specific enough that I can identify them?

1. Professional association serving my target market (consult Gales Directory of Associations or National Trade and Professional Associations Directory):

   _____

   _____

   _____

   _____

   _____

   _____

2. Conferences my target market attends:

   _____

   _____

   _____

   _____

   _____

   _____

3. Trade journals, magazines, ezines, and other publications my target audience reads (see also www.srds.com – Standard Rate and Data Service):

   _____

   _____

   _____

   _____

   _____

   _____

4. Where my target audience lives:

_____

_____

_____

_____

_____

_____

5. Radio programs my target audience listens to:

_____

_____

_____

_____

_____

6. Television shows my target market watches:

_____

_____

_____

_____

_____

_____

7. Web sites my target audience visits:

_____

_____

_____

_____

_____

_____

B. Viability:

Are there enough of them to make a viable client pool? Check the resources below which you will consult to determine the size of your market:

_____ Industry association surveys – contact the same associations you identified in defining your market to see if they have surveyed their membership and get access to that data.

_____ Census data such as that contained at http://www.census.gov/

_____ Labor force data at sites such as http://www.bls.gov

_____ Keyword searches relating to what you plan to offer – how many are searching for that term/service? Use http://www.overture.com or Google Suggest http://www.google.com/webhp?complete=1&hl=en

Can I reach them with a moderate marketing budget? Email or online is cheapest! Could you do that plus postcard mailings, free teleseminars, etc.?

____ yes

____ no

C.   Knowledge Worker Traits

Have I kept the traits of the Knowledge worker in mind as I crafted my market?

Addressed?	Knowledge Age Workers
	1. 10-14 careers during life
	2. *Fulfillment Ethic:* I choose the career(s) I wish, which gives me the greatest personal satisfaction.
	3. I am a better person, and therefore a better family member, when I am fulfilled at work.
	4. Key value: creativity, connection.
	5. Intuition accepted as companion to intellect.
	6. Immediate rewards.
	7. Participative, person-centered, decentralized management; "flat" organizations.
	8. Fringe benefits tailored to individual needs (e.g., cafeteria plans; flexwork).
	9. Entrepreneurs and smaller businesses dominate (85% of US Gross National Product).
	10. Information is key economic and societal base; change occurs rapidly.
	11. Individuals encouraged to create new job categories.
	12. Diverse workforce both ethnically and generationally; different values and priorities.
	13. Holistic philosophy: work and play blend; life/work balance key.

CHAPTER 3
Step 2: Identifying Your Core Message to Solve Your Market's Primary Problem

The following exercises will help you clarify both your Core Message and your market's Primary Problem.

Core Message Exercises

10 Clues to Discovering Your Life's Purpose	
1	What do you love to do, whether in your spare time or at work?
2	What parts of your present job or life activities do you thoroughly enjoy?
3	What do you naturally do well?
4	What are your ten greatest successes to date (in your eyes)? 1 2 3

	4
	5
	6
	7
	8
	9
	10
5	Is there a cause about which you feel passionate?
6	What are the ten most important lessons you have learned in your life?
	1
	2
	3
	4
	5
	6
	7
	8
	9
	10
7	Are there some issues or perceived problems that have occurred over and over again?
8	What do you daydream about doing or being?

9	Imagine you are writing your epitaph. What things do you want to be remembered for at the end of your life?
10	What would you do if you knew you could not fail?

Now, narrow down your responses to glean the 10 most important aspects of your life purpose and write any themes you notice here:

_____

_____

_____

_____

_____

To compose your life's purpose statement, synthesizing your responses to the Clues, use the following format:

"My life's purpose is to_____ [ESSENCE] _____ through [EXPRESSION] _____ ."

What is your life's purpose? Write your life's purpose statement here:

"My life's purpose is to _____ through _____ ."

What is your Unique Ability? (see textbook page 34 and *Unique Ability* by Catherine Nomura and Julia Waller).

_____

_____

_____

_____

_____

What are your 5 Signature Strengths?   Use the text *Now Discover Your Strengths* by Marcus Buckingham and the code you'll find in the book to access your own *Strengthsfinder 2.0* results.

1._____

2._____

3. _____

4. _____

5. _____

What are your expertise areas (or "horizontal niches")?

_____

_____

_____

_____

_____

Now, based on all of these exercises:

What is your Core Message?   (the subject, value, lesson, or area of focus about which you have the most passion and energy – that you would talk about, write about, contribute to or help people with, whether you got paid or not)

_____

_____

_____

_____

_____

_____

_____

Congratulations! Now we're going to temper this by learning more about our target audience's needs to finalize the process and prepare to test it.

Primary Problem Exercises

Using the 8 strategies which begin on page 40 of the text, list the results of your Primary Problem research below:

1.   Keyword research:

_____

_____

_____

_____

_____

2.   Trade publication research: (HINT: read up to 2 years of the articles in the primary trade journal for your industry to find out recurring themes and "hot buttons")

_____

_____

_____

_____

_____

3.   Ask campaign results (using www.askcampaignsforcoaches.com):

_____

_____

_____

_____

_____

4.   Online survey results:

_____

_____

_____

_____

_____

5.   Informal networking survey results:

_____

_____

_____

_____

6.   Phone survey results:

_____

_____

_____

_____

7.   R&D (research and development) team results:

_____

_____

_____

_____

8.   Blog feedback:

_____

_____

_____

_____

One of your goals here is to find an **underserved niche** (example: practice-building programs for a particular type of professionals existed at $2500 and $99 but nothing in between, so a moderate priced option would be appealing).

_____

_____

You can also review the **Yellow Pages ads** for others serving your proposed target market – are there some common selling points that everyone seems to be using? How could you distinguish your services?

_____

_____

My Market's Primary Problem (as I now understand it) is:

_____

_____

_____

_____

_____

My proposed solution will use (circle all that apply):

- Step-by-step approach/system
- Case Studies
- Narrative stories/testimonials
- Other

My Unique Selling/Serving Proposition (how I will distinguish myself) is:

_____

_____

(Remember, you can use delivery method, price, market, unique combination of products, turnaround time, elite vs. run-of-the-mill, etc. to create your USP.)

Later on, we'll explore media on which you'll deliver the solution.

PART TWO:

STARTING

CHAPTER 4
Step 3: Transitioning to Infopreneurship and Starting Your Business

More than 465,000 new businesses will be started this month – will yours be one of them?

MY TRANSITION PATH

Check the path below that best describes how you are (or did) transitioning to career coaching:

☐ Laid off from previous job
☐ Currently employed but dissatisfied – plan to use coaching to enrich current job
☐ Currently employed but dissatisfied – plan to leave job and start coaching business
☐ Author of career book that wants to add profit center
☐ Recruiter that wants to get paid for "free" advice to candidates by adding profit center
☐ Trainer (internal or independent) that wants to enhance results and impact with coaching

---

MY TRANSITION CHECKLIST

☐ Take coach training program to learn coaching, using company tuition reimbursement benefits or alternately, finance coach training myself
☐ Using what I've learned about my Intended Audience and Core Message (solving their Primary Problem), schedule evening or Saturday workshop OR write short (less than 25 pages) Special Report and offer discount on coaching package
☐ Start working with coaching clients – by phone or in person – one evening per week or Saturday mornings
☐ Choose and file paperwork on business name, start web design, etc. (see Starting Business Checklist below)
☐ Once I feel confident in my coaching skills and have 10 or more clients part-time, leave full-time job to do coaching business full-time (or my own hours, whatever they may be!)

STARTING BUSINESS CHECKLIST

___   Choose and register business name with the state in which you'll be doing business

___   Simultaneously, check availability and register your domain name on the internet (may be identical to business name)

___   Write mission statement

___   Consult with attorney

___   Choose business location

___   Contact county planner and city officials re: land use

___   Sign lease (if applicable)

___   Consult with accountant

___   See banker: open business checking account and discuss loan (if needed)

___   Decide on legal form of business (proprietorship, partnership, corporation, LLC)

___   File articles of incorporation if you incorporate, or articles of organization if LLC

___   Apply for taxpayer ID numbers (federal and state)

___   Write to IRS for Tax Guide for Small Business (or get online at www.irs.ustreas.gov)

___   Obtain business license for the city/county in which you'll do business

___   Purchase necessary equipment including computer, printer, fax service (can use efax www.efax.com or www.faxaway.com in lieu of a fax machine), and appropriate software including word processing (e.g. Word), bookkeeping (e.g. Quicken or Quickbooks), client/practice   management (for coaches, www.clientcompass.com is a great tool), email management, calendaring (e.g., Palm or Outlook), etc.

___   Contact insurance agent to discuss coverage for liability (for coaches, The Hartford has a special coaches' liability plan), your computer (usually not covered by homeowners), medical, disability, casualty, loss of business, etc.

___   Obtain any other necessary licenses or permits for your type of business

___   Contact sources for raw materials and distributors

___   Set up bookkeeping system

___   Draft business plan including start-up costs, financial projections, product description, target markets, reasons why you'll be successful, potential obstacles, how you'll handle

___   Design and launch web site

___   Determine whether to have separate business phone number; if so, get yellow pages listing in your city/town and on the internet

___   Determine whether to have toll-free "vanity" number (e.g. numbers that spell something related to your business); contact broker of phone numbers or web sites that offer these

___   Print business cards and, if needed, letterhead

___   Design and print brochure or flyer, if needed

___   Research and develop marketing strategy

___   File any needed trademarks, copyrights, etc.

___ Prepare your intake packet, client contract forms (get an attorney's input), other forms

___ Begin to test and implement marketing strategy (will include identifying professional associations, journals, publications, and conferences that you may want to target to speak at or write for to get yourself known among your target market, as well as strategies to generate referrals)

___ Announce launch (if virtual) or grand opening (if physical office or site) of business with an approach letter to your existing contacts, offering a "special rate" or other incentive to begin using your services

NOTE: For additional details on start-up, see *Launch Your Practice:Start-up from A to Z* by Marcia Bench and available here:
http://www.careercoachinstitute.com/books-launch.htm

MY FEE SETTING CALCULATOR

The most successful coaches use a formula to determine their fees. Here's how it works:

Fee Computation Worksheet

1.   Annual Income Goal $_____

How much do you want to make as *net* (after expenses) from your practice each year? One way to determine this, if you are just leaving a salaried job, is to add 10 to 15 percent to your previous salary – giving yourself a raise to compensate for the risk of going into your own business! – and use that as your goal. (This is only to calculate your *coaching* monthly fee, so if you expect to have income from other activities, exclude that from this computation.)

2.   Annual Overhead $_____

Now, analyze what costs you have that are related to your doing business. Note: just because you're running a home-based business and perhaps already have the computer system you'll be using does *not* mean that you don't have other overhead! Here are some typical overhead items:

OVERHEAD CALCULATION
(Monthly amounts – average if necessary)

Office rent	$
Clerical support	$
Telephone	$
Postage	$
Copying/printing	$
Automotive	$
Employment taxes	$
Personnel benefits	$
Insurance	$
Licenses	$
Publications	$
Professional dues	$
Stationery and supplies	$
Accounting and legal services	$
Travel	$
Office equipment	$
Marketing (25-30% of your time x your Daily Labor Rate – see below	$
Professional development (10% of your time x your Daily Labor Rate – see below)	$
TOTAL:	$

NOTE: Only list **indirect expenses** here; direct expenses (i.e. those which you wouldn't have incurred unless you were doing this project) are charged to clients!

Note: This overhead calculation includes appropriate amounts of your time spent marketing and doing professional development, so that you end up actually getting paid for those otherwise non-billable time.

3.   **Subtotal** (add 1 and 2) $_____

Now, add the figures in number 1 and 2 to get a subtotal.

4.   **Profit** (10-25%) $_____

Next, add a profit margin of anywhere from 10 to 25 percent. (After all, you're not in this business just to break even, right?)

5.   **Annual Revenue Goal** $_____

Now, add items 3 and 4 to get your annual revenue goal. But you're not finished yet! You still need to calculate what this means per month:

6.　　Divide A.R.G. (#5 above) by 12 to

**　　　get monthly goal　　　　　　　　　　\$_____**

7.　　Divide A.R.G. (#5 above) by the monthly fee you want to charge to see how many clients you need for a full practice

And finally, you need to figure out how many clients, at what rate, you will need

to be working with to meet this monthly goal. You can continue to adjust the

variables until the number of clients and the monthly fee are in line with your

desired number of working hours.

Here's an example:

EXAMPLE:

1.	Annual Income Goal	\$100,000	
2.	Annual Overhead	\$ 53,000	(\$50,000 expenses + marketing and profess-ional development time per formula on overhead computation sheet)
3.	Subtotal	\$153,000	
4.	Profit (10% of subtotal)	\$ 15,300	
5.	Annual Revenue Goal	\$168,300	
6.	Divided by 12 months =	\$ 14,025	
7.	Scenario 1: Divided by \$500/mo = 28 clients		
	Scenario 2: Divided by \$750/mo = 19 client/mo.		

　　(Could also divide by desired number of clients to determine monthly fee, e.g., divide \$14,025 by 20 clients = \$700 each to meet goal)

Final step: determine whether number of clients is feasible to see within, e.g. 12.5 days/month to be billed (depending on what a "day" is for you – 3 hours? 4 hours? 6 hours?). See next section to help you determine your billable days per month.

Try it yourself on the worksheet that follows.

FEE COMPUTATION WORKSHEET

1.   **Annual Income Goal** $_____

      (previous salary of $_____ plus 10-15%
      raise of $_____ = $_____)

2.   **Overhead** $_____

3.   **Subtotal** $_____

4.   **Profit** (10-25%) $_____

5.   **Annual Revenue Goal** $_____

6.   **Divide A.R.G. (#5 above) by 12 to**
     get monthly goal $_____

7.   **Divide A.R.G. (#5 above) by the**
monthly fee you want to charge to see
how many clients you need for a full practice   _____ **clients at**
$_____

Daily Labor Rate

The one remaining variable that you must compute is your Daily Labor Rate – that is, how much income – on average – you must generate daily from coaching to meet your goals. It's not as simple as dividing your annual income goal by 365, since you won't be working 365 days per year. But how many days *will* you work? That is an individual choice. But let me suggest that, at a minimum, you deduct:

- 104 weekend days (52 weeks x 2 days)
- 10 vacation days
- 5 days of professional development (or more, depending on you)
- 48 days of marketing time (4 days/month = 25% of your total time)

That totals 167 days, deducted from 365 leaves 198 potentially billable days. You may also wish to deduct a certain number of days (maybe 10 percent of the total or another 20 days) for practice management and administration, since that is not billable time. So that leaves you with 178 days, the number you divide into your annual income goal (item 1 in the formula) to get your Daily Labor Rate.

Annual income goal   Example: $100,000
$100,000/178 = $560 per day = Daily Labor Rate

You multiply this by 4 days per month (25% of 12.5 billable days) for marketing in your overhead calculation, and by 1 day per month (10% of 12.5 billable days) for professional development

Once you have determined your basic rate, use these guidelines to set your final fee level:

1. Compare your daily billing rate to the median rates charged by others in your specialty
2. Modifying factors to fee as computed:

    i. What the competition is charging
    ii. Your geographic location
    iii. Your degree of specialty, amount of experience, uniqueness in field and any additional credentials or qualifications

3. If you travel to meet with a client face to face, it is typical to charge a "per diem" fee that includes hotel, meals, ground transportation, and incidentals (air fare is billed as a direct expense). Average range: $200 to $400, depending on geographic location.

Here are some additional tools you may wish to use in your business start-up:

VIRTUAL TOOLS CHECKLIST

Tool	Applicable?	Provider Used
Internet Tools		
Web hosting company		
News/discussion groups		
Real-time chat		
Merchant account		
Shopping cart (we recommend http://www.shoppingcartforcoaches.com)		
Newsletter/mailing list management		
Client/market surveys (we recommend http://www.surveymonkey.com)		
Web conferencing		
Blogging setup provider		
Email distribution/list management (we recommend http://www.shoppingcartforcoaches.com)		
Telephone Tools		
Bridge lines		
Voiceover IP phone		
Long distance services		
Vanity 800 numbers		
Phone answering service (e.g., http://www.workeasy.com)		
Fax (http://www.faxaway.com)		
Software Tools		
Practice management		
Small business accounting/bookkeeping		
Tax return preparation		
Other:		

VENDOR CHECKLIST

Type of Vendor	Applicable?	Date Obtained
Virtual Assistant		
Bookkeeper		
Graphic designer		
Web designer		
Copywriter		
Shopping cart specialist		
Attorney		
Certified Public Accountant		
Search Engine Optimization Specialist		
CD/audio duplication specialist		
Fulfillment service		
Print-on-demand book printing company		

INSURANCE CHECKLIST

Type of Insurance	Applicable?	Date Obtained
Business casualty/theft insurance		
Business liability insurance		
Professional liability insurance		
Errors and omissions insurance		
Health insurance (for you and employees)		
Disability insurance		
Workers compensation insurance		
Auto insurance (for company vehicle)		
Business interruption insurance		
Life insurance		
Other insurance		

PERMITS AND LICENSES CHECKLIST

Type of Permit	Applicable?	Date Obtained
Business name registration		
Home office permit (county, city)		
Business license (county, city)		
Occupational license, if any		
Building/remodeling permit		
Articles of incorporation or LLC organization (see next chapter)		
IRS Employer ID Number*		
State Employer ID Number *		
Other permits		

You will also have to determine whether or not to incorporate (vs. operating as a sole proprietor, a Limited Liability Company, or a partnership)

MY STRATEGIC PARTNER/VENDOR CHECKLIST

- ☐ Professional
- ☐ Responsive
- ☐ Personal responsibility
- ☐ Clear agreements
- ☐ Resourceful
- ☐ Referral minded

MY BUSINESS VISION STATEMENT:

_____

_____

_____

_____

_____

_____

_____

_____

_____

_____

_____

_____

_____

_____

CHAPTER 5
Step 4: Honing Your Infopreneur Skills

Throughout this chapter, remember the Infopreneur Cycle:

My First Speech or Seminar:

1. Topic: _____

2. Title: _____
   Use the power words page 71 text as well as the following formats:

- Who else wants…?
- How _____ made me___?
- How to _____
- 7 Secrets to _____

3. Presentation outline:

Minute	Content
0-5	Greeting:
-5-10	Verbal picture of my audience's Primary Problem: 5 benefits of my your solution/Core Message: 1. 2. 3. 4. 5.
10-17	Point number 1 of your solution: Statistic: Case study/example: Benefits/what's in it for the listener:
17-22	Point number 2 of your solution: Statistic: Case study/example: Benefits/what's in it for the listener:
22-27	Point number 3 of your solution: Statistic: Case study/example: Benefits/what's in it for the listener:
27-30	Initial pitch/upsell:

30-35	Optional Q&A
35-40	Point number 4 of your solution: t Statistic: Case study/example: Benefits/what's in it for the listener:
40-45	Guest(s) I'll use as spotlight presentation/testimonial:
45-50	Point number 5 of your solution: Statistic: Case study/example: Benefits/what's in it for the listener:
50-55	Second pitch/upsell:
55-60	Final questions, sign-off greeting

4. Where/how you will test your message/presentation (free teleseminar, free speech to service club, etc.):

_____

_____

_____

_____

_____

5. Fee I will charge for my seminar or teleseminar:

6. Who I will use to record my seminar or teleseminar:
    (www.nocostconference.com includes recording for free; we recommend Audio Strategies for professional teleseminar recording)

7. Incentives/bonuses I'll give for attendance: (remember, these don't have to be your products! You can make arrangements with another author or speaker to give/sell their products here too!)

_____

_____

_____

_____

_____

8. My promotion strategies:

_____

_____

_____

_____

_____

9. My "back of the room" products to upsell:

_____

_____

_____

_____

_____

10. My follow-up strategy:

_____

_____

_____

_____

_____

My Coaching Delivery Model(s)

Indicate on the checklist below which models you will use in your coaching package for each target market you serve:

Coaching Delivery Method	Market #1 (Y/N)	Market #2 (Y/N)	Market #3 (Y/N)
One-on-one coaching + products			
Membership community			
Group coaching			
Laser coaching/coaching gym			
Renewable month-to-month contract			
Mastermind group/inner circle			

My First Article

NOTE: The points you use in your first seminar, workshop or teleseminar above can also be used for your first article or ebook!

1.   Key points my audience needs to know about my Core Message (3-5 points for one-hour teleseminar, up to 10 points for book or ebook)

1	
2	
3	
4	
5	
6	
7	

8	
9	
10	

How could you leverage your initial Special Report into a larger pipeline of products through which you could take your target audience?

Here's an example:

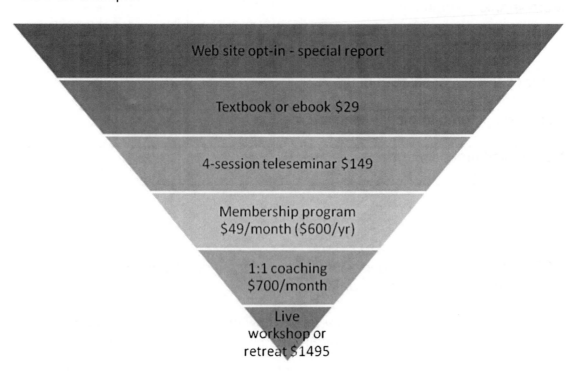

CHAPTER 6
Step 5: Using Manifesting Principles to Attract What You Desire

Law #1: You are a co-creator of your world, from the inside out.

If you could use your "magic wand" to create anything you want in the next 6-12 months, what would you create?

Do you find yourself blaming anything in your past for the way you and your life are today? What?

Law #2: You attract what you focus on, in thought and emotion.

Think of one thing you have successfully focused on and then attracted in your life that you strongly desired. Describe it here:

Now identify one goal or desired experience you have for your career infopreneur business and write it here:

Now, turn this desire into an affirmative statement – as though you already have it – and write it here:

Be sure to focus on the experience of having this thing – not its absence – as you move toward it becoming reality for you!

Remember the Attraction Formula as you do:

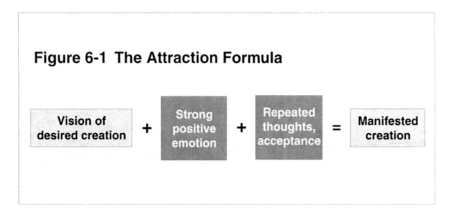

Figure 6-1 The Attraction Formula

Law #3: Your intention prepaves your experience.

Often it helps to have an "anchor" to help us remember a new habit, such as intending each "segment" of our day. What word could you say, or image could you post in your work area and/or home to remind you to practice segment intending for the next 3-4 weeks?

Law #4: To experience it, you must allow it in and believe you deserve it.

Can you identify any beliefs you hold about yourself or your work/business that are sabotaging or otherwise holding you back from receiving all the good you could imagine? Write them down here:

_____

_____

_____

_____

Now, what new belief could you repeat to yourself to replace each of the sabotaging beliefs you listed above? Write them down here:

_____

_____

_____

_____

Law #5: Everything is created twice, in mind and in physical form.

Dr. Deepak Chopra teaches that 90 percent of today's thoughts are *identical* to the ones we thought yesterday! To test this finding, for the next 7 days, keep a journal, updated at least hourly, of what your dominant thoughts and feelings are – the ones that are most prevalent in your mind and emotions.

Then, at the end of the 7 days (or longer if you wish!), go back through your journal and highlight (or otherwise capture) themes. Ask yourself:

Are these the thoughts and feelings that will create the successful career infopreneur business you desire?

If not, what thoughts and feelings would I like to entertain again that *will* create the future I desire?

Law #6: The essential you is much bigger than you think.

Take in the notion that you are *already* connected to everything you desire – that you simply need to create the right environment to allow it into your life. Breathe that in…and let it become a living awareness as you go through your day today!

Law #7: To create what you want requires that you trust the process.

Do you consider yourself more of a trusting or a naturally suspicious person?

What would have to happen for you to trust your own process of growth more?

Can you think of a role model who you could emulate that trusts and flows with their own unique process?

Law #8: What you focus on multiplies.

In his *Personal Power* series, Tony Robbins suggests the idea of asking a "power question" upon awakening, such as "How can I make this the best day of my life?"

What technique could you use to start your day off right, so that the good you desire multiplies at every turn?

Law #9: Your feelings guide what you create, and your feelings can be changed.

Consider the possibility that you are not at the mercy of your feelings – but they are simply *feedback* which you can change at any time.

How are you feeling now?

Is this the best feeling you can imagine? If not, toward what feeling would you like to reach to improve your feeling state?

Practice this process throughout your day and watch the amazing results unfold.

Law #10: Appreciate and generously circulate your good to attract more.

Finally, practice keeping an "appreciation log" every day, either upon awakening or just before you go to bed.

Just start out, "I appreciate…" and write as many things, people, and situations in your life as you can that you are grateful for.

Then, keep a lookout for your life to improve and for more of what you want to show up – appreciation is an accelerant of attraction!

PART THREE:

TRAVELING

CHAPTER 7
Step 6: Marketing Your Services Online – Web Strategies That Work

Do you have a plan for both "marketing" and for "selling" in your business, as defined in this chapter?

How are you doing with implementing practices of high-income coaches? Answer the questions below to see.

Question	Yes	No
Have a clear niche and brand that is communicated through all they do		
Make marketing their primary focus and do marketing activities every day		
Focus on what revenue-generating activities while planning their day		
Package their services		
Have created information products that they sell with coaching and other services		
Lead with an information product, not coaching, when marketing		
Choose marketing strategies that are less expensive but more effective, including referral-based marketing, affiliate marketing, writing and speaking		
Expect their clients to become lifetime clients, not just 90-day engagements		
Continue to provide additional value to their existing and new clients through new products and services (some that they create, some offered through strategic alliance partners)		
Have a plan for entry, execution, and exit from their business		
Have created a product funnel that allows customers to access them at a variety of price points		
Take a long-term, strategic view of their business and know how each element of their product funnel fits together toward their long-term goals		

My Marketing Strategies

Please indicate below what percentage of the time you *currently* use each of the strategies below, and what you want to be doing *ideally,* remembering that top-earning coaches focus primarily on strategies 4, 5 and 6:

Marketing Strategy	Current %	Ideal %
1. Cold calls		
2. Direct mail brochures/Sales letters to cold lists		
3. No-charge coaching or consultation sessions to pre-qualified leads		
4. Referral-based promotion		
5. Speaking, seminars, and teleseminars		
6. Writing articles, books, newsletters		

My Marketing Methods

In the table below, please highlight at least two marketing methods in each column that you are using – or plan to use – to market your career coaching services.

Online	Offline	Can be Online or Offline
Web site	Free speech, seminar or workshop	Article publication, placement, syndication
Articles and Special Reports	Trade show exhibit and/or presentation	Book (marketed online, available in print)
Ezine	Lead box at third party business	Referrals from vendors, others
Email broadcasts	Lead sharing party	Directory listing
Ebook	Coaching demonstration	Publicity/press releases
Free teleseminar	Quizzes	Gift certificate for products or series
Online audio clips	Expert interview on tv or radio	Third-party catalog sales of books, CD's
Podcast	Networking meeting	Product/service catalog
Virtual Book Tour	Postcards, direct mail	Flyers, brochures
Online video clips	Book signing	Word of mouth
Online infomercial	Informational label on shipping box	Testimonials
Google adwords	24/7 telephone information line	Case studies
E-course, autoresponder sequences	Contingent Coaching Session	Survey
Social network marketing	Print newsletter	Upselling and cross-selling to existing customers
Interviews using Ask	Classified ad	

campaigns		
Affiliate promotions		
Blog		
Webinar		

My Marketing Cycle

Use the following checklist to guide you through launching your marketing:

Step	Check When Done
1. Begin building mailing list	
2. Start ezine	
3. Launch web site	
4. Create first info product	
5. Package services (drawing from elements in next table – highlight those you plan to use)	

Items to Package With Career Coaching:

You Create/Provide	Third Party/Partner Creates/Provides	Can be Either You or Third Party
Networking or Mastermind group (live or via conference line)	Assessments	Coaching (if you train or license others)
Live workshops, seminars or boot camps	Salary and benefits data service	Quizzes (can use assessmentgenerator.com)
Teleseminars	Resume distribution (we recommend resumespider.com)	Resume writing

Inner Circle (e.g., careerinfopreneur.com/ innercircle.html)	Job search tracking software (we recommend cbizsoft.com)	Resume critique
	Directories of corporations, associations, venture capitalists, recruiters	Learning through e-course
	Job board search, listing assistance (we recommend workgiant.com)	Interview coaching
	Web portfolios for your clients (we recommend brandego.com)	Cover letter writing
		Books, e-books, CD's, DVD's
		Salary negotiation coaching
		Reference checking service (can use allisontaylor.com)
		Image coaching
		Subscription newsletter (can get content from ezinearticles.com, ideamarketers.com or customizednewsletters.com)

CHAPTER 8
Step 7: Marketing Your Services Offline – Keeping Your Pipeline Full

List below the steps on your Staircase of Trust, listing strategy on left and desired outcome on right. Here is an example:

Strategy	Outcome
Squeeze/opt-in page	Join mailing list
Online sales letter	Purchase info product

Strategy	Outcome

Following are three checklists of offline and quasi-offline strategies for you to consider. Please check each as currently in use in your business, something you plan to implement in next 6-12 months, or something you do not plan to use.

Offline – Done by You Personally	Using now	Plan to Use	Will not use
Free speech, seminar or workshop			
Trade show exhibit and/or presentation			
Lead box at third party business			
Lead sharing party			
Coaching demonstration			
Quizzes			
Expert interview on tv or radio			
Networking meeting			
Postcards, direct mail			
Book signing or virtual book tour via teleseminar			
Informational label on shipping box			
24/7 telephone information line			
Contingent Coaching Session			
Print newsletter			
Classified ad			

Offline – Done by You OR Third Party	Using now	Plan to Use	Will not use
Coaching (e.g. having coaches work under or with you)			
Resume writing			
Resume critique			
E-course			
Interview coaching			
Cover letter writing			
Books, e-books, CD's, DVD's			
Salary negotiation coaching			
Reference checking			
Image coaching			
Subscription newsletter			

Offline OR Online	Using now	Plan to Use	Will not use
Article publication, placement, syndication			
Book (marketed online, available in print)			
Referrals from vendors, others			
Directory listing			
Publicity/press releases			
Gift certificate for products or series			
Third-party catalog sales of books, CD's			
Product/service catalog			
Flyers, brochures			
Word of mouth			
Testimonials			
Case studies			
Survey			
Upselling and cross-selling to existing customers			

PART FOUR:

ARRIVING

CHAPTER 9: Step 8: Balancing Personal and Work Life as an Entrepreneur

1. Deciding what is important

Below, write your eulogy:

_____

_____

_____

_____

_____

What are 100 lifetime goals you would like to accomplish?

1.
2.
3.
4.
5.
6.
7.
8.
9.
10.
11.
12.
13.
14.
15.
16.
17.
18.
19.
20.
21.
22.
23.
24.
25.
26.
27.
28.

29.
30.
31.
32.
33.
34.
35.
36.
37.
38.
39.
40.
41.
42.
43.
44.
45.
46.
47.
48.
49.
50.
51.
52.
53.
54.
55.
56.
57.
58.
59.
60.
61.
62.
63.
64.
65.
66.
67.
68.
69.
70.
71.
72.
73.
74.

75.
76.
77.
78.
79.
80.
81.
82.
83.
84.
85.
86.
87.
88.
89.
90.
91.
92.
93.
94.
95.
96.
97.
98.
99.
100.

List at least 50 famous (or not so famous) people you would like to meet in your lifetime:

1.
2.
3.
4.
5.
6.
7.
8.
9.
10.
11.
12.
13.
14.
15.

16.
17.
18.
19.
20.
21.
22.
23.
24.
25.
26.
27.
28.
29.
30.
31.
32.
33.
34.
35.
36.
37.
38.
39.
40.
41.
42.
43.
44.
45.
46.
47.
48.
49.
50.

2. Friends

With whom do you spend most of your time…

Professionally:

_____

_____

_____

_____

_____

Personally:

_____

_____

_____

_____

_____

3. Personal vs. Work Life.

How do you separate personal from work life?

_____

_____

_____

_____

_____

4. Multitasking vs. Focus.

What can you to do minimize multitasking and increase focus in your life and business?

_____

_____

_____

_____

_____

5. Plan Time Off.

How many days a week would you like to work?

How much vacation will you take this year?

_____

_____

_____

Write the dates of your vacations here:

_____

_____

6. Power Hours.

What hours of the day will you dedicate as your "power hours"?

_____

_____

How long will you commit to do this process before you decide whether it is right for you?

_____

_____

7. Goals – Personal and Work.

Evaluate your goals for the past year. What % were work-related?

_____

_____

How can you incorporate more personal and relationship goals this year?

_____

_____

_____

_____

_____

8. Delegating.

What are you now doing that someone else could/should do?

_____

_____

_____

_____

_____

What additional staff, vendors, or volunteers do you need to help you in those areas?

_____

_____

_____

_____

_____

9. Exercise.

How much do you currently exercise each day? Each week?

_____

_____

If you would like to increase this, what are you willing to commit to? What kinds of activities?

_____

_____

_____

_____

_____

10. Meditation.

How much do you currently meditate and/or pray each day? Each week?

_____

If you would like to increase this, what are you willing to commit to? What kinds of processes?

_____

_____

_____

_____

_____

CHAPTER 10: Step 9 – Creating Wealth and Playing a Bigger Game

Wealth Creation Principles for Career Infopreneurs

Supplemental Resource: *No B.S. Guide to Wealth Attraction for Entrepreneurs* by Dan Kennedy.

1. **Adopt the beliefs of a wealth builder.** What beliefs were you taught as a child about money? List them here.

_____

_____

_____

_____

_____

_____

_____

_____

_____

_____

_____

Do you believe these principles? Or are there others that would serve you better? Consider the examples below:

- I have access to an unlimited, abundant source of money, clients, time, and other resources that support my success.
- I deserve to be wealthy; it is my natural state.
- I release past beliefs and experiences that do not serve my new state of wealth and abundance. That was then; this is now!
- I am on my way to becoming a millionaire now!
- I freely give and receive money with a consciousness of abundance.
- My money works hard for me and creates an ongoing stream of good for myself and others.
- I accept and embrace only those thoughts, beliefs and experiences that support my wealth.

Write out your chosen NEW beliefs about money here:

_____

_____

_____

_____

_____

_____

_____

_____

_____

2. Decide and commit to becoming wealthy.

What is your annual income goal? $_____

What does that represent in income per week? $_____

Per day? $_____

My mentor Alex Mandossian has developed a great challenge question: "What must happen to make it inevitable that [I achieve my desired result]"? One of his favorites: "What must happen to make it inevitable that my annual income becomes my monthly income?"

What is *your* challenge question to move you closer to your financial goals?

_____

_____

_____

_____

3. Challenge your own upper limits.

List a situation below, whether in business or personal life, where you unconsciously sabotaged yourself when your own "upper limits" were reached:

_____

_____

_____

How will you avoid this pattern in the future?

_____

_____

_____

4. **Create a wealth cycle, not a lifestyle cycle.**

Which of these cycles most characterizes you now?

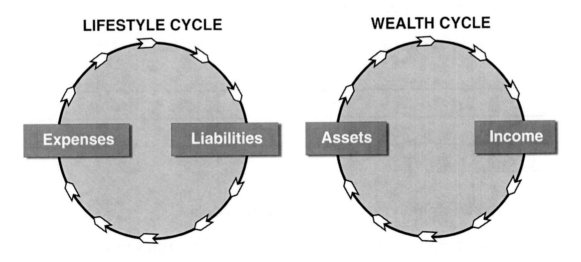

What can you start doing in the next 30 days to move more into the wealth-creation cycle?

_____

_____

_____

_____

5. **Focus on the opportunities ahead of you, not problems or obstacles.**

Think about a "problem" you have had or are facing in establishing or growing your business. How can you think of it differently ("challenge" or "question awaiting an answer") to take a more positive approach?

_____

_____

_____

6. Confidently promote your services; don't allow fear to stop you.

What is your current comfort level with promoting and selling your infopreneur services. (Use a 1 to 5 scale, 5 being the highest) _____

Do you ever let fear stop you from progressing, professionally or personally? ____ yes; ____ no

If so, what can you do next time to transcend your fear?

_____

_____

_____

_____

7. Associate with successful, wealthy people.

Who are the 5 people with whom you spend most of your time?

1. _____

2. _____

3. _____

4. _____

5. _____

List 5 wealthy people you would like to meet:

1. _____

2. _____

3. _____

4. _____

5. _____

8. Remember, you are paid based on your results, not on how much time you work. How can you begin adding even more value to what you sell to your customers or clients so that you get even better results?

_____

_____

_____

10 Financial Habits for Success

1. Set revenue targets for both active and passive income.

How much of your income do you want to come from active sources? $_____

Passive? $ _____

2. Plan and control expenses. Is there a way to save money spent on manual
input of certain data by purchasing a software program or web plug-in for one of your business processes?

Could you save money by changing vendors for certain items you purchase regularly?

Could you eliminate some expenses entirely?

Delegate more?

Should you incorporate to take advantage of more tax advantages?

3. Plan what you will do with your profits. What do you plan to do with the profits you make from your business? Look back at your 100 lifetime goals in the prior chapter and see if those don't spark some ideas.

4. Tithe 10 percent of all you earn. Do you currently tithe to one or more charities? ___yes; ___no. Do you plan to start? ___yes; ___no. What percentage? ___

5. Manage your money well by having multiple accounts. Consider Harv Eker's suggested financial allocation strategy:

- 10% into a "give" account (your tithe)
- 10% to a Financial Freedom Account – 10 percent of every after-tax dollar you receive goes into this fund; it is to be used only for investments and purchasing passive income streams. (Loral Langemeier calls this your Wealth Account)
- 10% to a Play Account – to use to nurture yourself and engage in what Thomas Leonard called Extraordinary Self-Care
- 10% into a Long-Term Savings For Spending Account – for extraordinary expenses and larger items you want (or need) to purchase
- 10% into an Education Account – for your professional development (see habit 10 below)
- 50% into a Necessities Account – to use for your monthly household expenses

Which of these are you already doing?

Which would you like to start within 30-60 days?

6. Mentor or coach for free; barter your services. How could you use pro bono mentoring or coaching or a bartering system to obtain some services or products you need for your business in exchange?

7. Raise your fees when you're too busy. Is it time to raise your fees? ___yes; ___no. Usually 10-15 percent is well received by clients. When will you start?

8. Create business systems that will help you manage growth. What business management systems do you plan to explore (a) now and (b) in the future to save you time and make you more money?

9. Plan how you will exit the business. What is your exit strategy for selling or leaving your business?

_____

_____

_____

10. Plan and continuously engage in personal and professional development. What is your approach to engage in continual professional development: daily Learning Hour? Quarterly educational conferences? Attend teleseminars or other online events?

_____

_____

_____

Business Growth Strategies: How High Do You Want to Go?

There are three basic ways to increase sales of your products and services:

a) Increase the number of sales of an existing product
b) Raise the price of your existing product (or bundle it differently)
c) Offer a new product to your current customers

Which of these would give you the most leverage at the point where your business is now? ___a; ___b; ____c

Strategy	Use? Y/N
1. Take your signature seminar national.	
2. Get published by a major publisher.	
3. Obtain national media coverage (print and television).	
4. Create an exclusive mastermind group and/or high-end retreat.	
5. Offer day-long consulting opportunities.	
6. License your content.	
7. Set up distributors for your products.	
8. Franchise your programs.	

About the Author and Career Coach Institute

Marcia Bench is known as the "Career Coaching Queen" with a 22-year history as a world-renowned expert in the field of career coaching and workplace trends. A Master Certified Career Coach,™ she has been coaching and consulting both individual and corporate clients since 1986. She is Founder/Director of Career Coach Institute, LLC, http://www.careercoachinstitute.com and Retirement Coach Institute, http://www.retirementcoachinstitute.com as well as other coaching and career development sites – see http://www.marciabench.com for full list.

A former attorney, Marcia has authored 20 previous books, including *Career Coaching: An Insider's Guide* (High Flight Press 2008). In addition, she has written *Thriving in Transition* (Simon & Schuster), *When 9 to 5 Isn't Enough* (Hay House), *Retire Your Way!,* and more.

Marcia has been a featured speaker/trainer at over 500 local, regional and national conferences, as well as a guest on numerous television and radio programs. Her mission is "changing the workplace, one worker at a time."

Marcia's coaching experience includes work with managers and executives from Fortune 500 firms in a variety of industries as well as dozens of business owners, professionals, and military officers entering the civilian workforce.

Prior to entering the coach training industry, Marcia was Senior Vice President in a dot-com career management firm for 4 years, and previously spent 10 years as President of New Work Directions, a business and consulting firm she founded. Ms. Bench developed her expertise in business start-up and management in part through her 4 years as a practicing attorney specializing in business and employment issues. She is a current member of the International Coach Federation.

Marcia's education includes a Juris Doctorate from Northwestern School of Law of Lewis & Clark College and a Bachelor of Science in Psychology from Western Oregon University. In addition, she is a Certified Career Management Practitioner through the International Board of Career Management Certification, a Certified Business Coach, a Certified Teleader and Master Certified Career Coach.

For further information, or to talk with Ms. Bench, contact:
Career Coach Institute
8269G SW Wilsonville Rd. #188
Wilsonville OR 97070
coach@careercoachinstitute.com
www.careercoachinstitute.com

ORDER FORM

We hope that you are enjoying this product! If you would like more information about our kits, we encourage you to visit http://www.careercoachinstitute.com, or copy and complete this form and fax it to 866-226-2244. Our physical mailing address is Career Coach Institute, 8269G SW Wilsonville Road #188, Wilsonville, OR 97070.

Name: _____

Address: _____

City, State, ZIP: _____

Country: _____

Home Telephone: _____

Work Telephone: _____

Fax: _____ Email: _____

How did you hear about us:

- ❏ Internet search
- ❏ Referred by a friend
- ❏ Heard one of the authors speak
- ❏ Read an article written by the authors
- ❏ Other: _____

Please send me information about:

- ❏ Your product catalog
- ❏ How to become a Certified Career Coach
- ❏ How to become a Certified Executive Career Coach
- ❏ How to start and expand my own coaching business
- ❏ Speaking to our group or event
- ❏ Customized training for our organization
- ❏ Other: _____

Thank you for your request!

Lightning Source UK Ltd.
Milton Keynes UK
UKOW011038180313

207823UK00001B/20/P